FAVOURITE
NURSERY
RHYMES

Illustrated by Peter Bowman

Bounty
Books

Designed by Alison Fenton

First published in 1988 by Conran Octopus Ltd
Reprinted 1989

This edition published in 2008 by Bounty Books,
a division of Octopus Publishing Group Ltd
2–4 Heron Quays, London E14 4JP
www.octopusbooks.co.uk
Reprinted 2009

An Hachette UK Company
www.hachette.co.uk

ISBN: 978-0-753718-15-5

A CIP catalogue record for this book is available from the British Library

Printed and bound in China

Hush-a-bye, baby, on the tree top,
When the wind blows, the cradle will rock;
When the bough breaks, the cradle will fall,
Down will come baby, cradle and all.

I Love Little Pussy

I love little pussy, her coat is so warm,
And if I don't hurt her, she'll do me no harm.
So I'll not pull her tail, nor drive her away,
But pussy and I very gently will play.

Old Mother Hubbard
Went to the cupboard,
To fetch her poor dog a bone.
But when she got there
The cupboard was bare,
And so the poor dog had none.

Ring-a-ring o'roses,
A pocket full of posies,
A-tishoo! A-tishoo!
We all fall down.

BOYS AND GIRLS, COME OUT TO PLAY

Boys and girls, come out to play,
The moon doth shine as bright as day.
Leave your supper and leave your sleep,
And join your playfellows into the street.
Come with a whoop and come with a call,
Come with a good will or not at all.
Up the ladder and down the wall,
A half-penny loaf will serve us all.
You find the milk and I'll find flour,
And we'll have a pudding in half an hour.

MARY HAD A LITTLE LAMB

Mary had a little lamb,
Its fleece was white as snow.
And everywhere that Mary went
The lamb was sure to go.

It followed her to school one day,
That was against the rule.
It made the children laugh and play
To see a lamb at school.

Mary, Mary, quite contrary,
How does your garden grow?
With silver bells and cockle shells,
And pretty maids all in a row.

Jack and Jill went up the hill
To fetch a pail of water.
Jack fell down and broke his crown,
And Jill came tumbling after.

Up Jack got and home did trot
As fast as he could caper.
He went to bed to mend his head
With vinegar and brown paper.

Under a Hill

There was an old woman
Lived under a hill,
And if she's not gone
She lives there still.

There was a Crooked Man

There was a crooked man,
And he walked a crooked mile,
He found a crooked sixpence
Against a crooked stile.
He bought a crooked cat,
Which caught a crooked mouse,
And they all lived together
In a little crooked house.

THE DONKEY

If I had a donkey that wouldn't go,
Would I beat him? No, no, no.
I'd put him in the barn and give him some corn.
The best little donkey that ever was born.

TOM, TOM, THE PIPER'S SON

Tom, Tom, the piper's son,
Stole a pig and away did run.
The pig was eat and Tom was beat,
And Tom went howling down the street.

THE GRAND OLD DUKE OF YORK

Oh, the grand old Duke of York,
He had ten thousand men.
He marched them up to the top of the hill,
And he marched them down again.
And when they were up, they were up,
And when they were down, they were down,
And when they were only half-way up,
They were neither up nor down.

Ride a cock-horse to Banbury Cross,
To see a fine lady upon a white horse.
Rings on her fingers and bells on her toes,
She shall have music wherever she goes.

Pussy cat, pussy cat,
Where have you been?
I've been up to London
To look at the Queen.

Pussy cat, pussy cat,
What did you there?
I frightened a little mouse
Under her chair.

Pretty maid, pretty maid,
Where have you been?
Gathering roses
To give to the Queen.

Pretty maid, pretty maid
What gave she you?
She gave me a diamond,
As big as my shoe.

COBBLER, COBBLER

Cobbler, cobbler, mend my shoe,
Get it done by half past two.

Stitch it up, and stitch it down,
Then I'll give you half a crown.

DOCTOR FOSTER

Doctor Foster went to Gloucester
In a shower of rain.
He stepped in a puddle,
Right up to his middle,
And never went there again.

Pat-a-cake, pat-a-cake, baker's man,
Bake me a cake as fast as you can.
Pat it and prick it, and mark it with B,
Put it in the oven for baby and me.

HERE WE GO ROUND
THE MULBERRY BUSH

Here we go round the mulberry bush,
The mulberry bush, the mulberry bush,
Here we go round the mulberry bush,
On a cold and frosty morning.

This is the way we clap our hands,
Clap our hands, clap our hands,
This is the way we clap our hands,
On a cold and frosty morning.

This is the way we wash our clothes,
Wash our clothes, wash our clothes,
This is the way we wash our clothes,
On a cold and frosty morning.

Sally Go Round the Sun

Sally go round the sun,
Sally go round the moon,
Sally go round the chimney-pots
On a Saturday afternoon.

THIS LITTLE PIG WENT TO MARKET

This little pig went to market,
This little pig stayed at home,
This little pig had roast beef,
This little pig had none,
And this little pig cried, Wee-wee-wee,
All the way home.

Dickery, dickery, dare,
The pig flew up in the air;
The man in brown
Soon brought him down,
Dickery, dickery, dare.

Sing a song of sixpence,
A pocket full of rye,
Four and twenty blackbirds,
Baked in a pie.

When the pie was opened,
The birds began to sing.
Was not that a dainty dish
To set before the king?

The king was in his counting-house,
Counting out his money.
The queen was in the parlour,
Eating bread and honey.

The maid was in the garden,
Hanging out the clothes,
When down came a blackbird
And pecked off her nose.

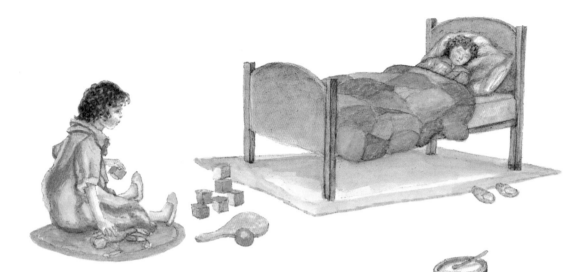 To Bed! to Bed! Says Sleepy-Head

To bed! to bed!
Says Sleepy-Head,
Tarry awhile,
Says Slow;
Put on the pan,
Says Greedy Nan,
Let's sup before we go.

DIDDLE, DIDDLE, DUMPLING

Diddle, diddle, dumpling, my son John,
Went to bed with his trousers on.
One shoe off, the other shoe on,
Diddle, diddle, dumpling, my son John.

I had a little nut tree,
Nothing would it bear
But a silver nutmeg
And a golden pear.

The King of Spain's daughter
Came to visit me,
And all for the sake
Of my little nut tree.

I skipped over water,
I danced over sea,
And all the birds in the air
Couldn't catch me.

Lavender's blue, dilly, dilly,
Lavender's green.
When I am king, dilly, dilly,
You shall be queen.
Call up your men, dilly, dilly,
Set them to work,
Some to the plough, dilly, dilly,
Some to the cart,
Some to make hay, dilly, dilly,
Some to cut corn,
Whilst you and I, dilly, dilly,
Keep ourselves warm.

Jack Sprat

Jack Sprat could eat no fat,
His wife could eat no lean,
And so, between them both, you see,
They licked the platter clean.

Little Jack Horner

Little Jack Horner
Sat in a corner,
Eating his Christmas pie.
He put in his thumb,
And pulled out a plum,
And said, What a good boy am I!

LITTLE TOMMY TUCKER

Little Tommy Tucker
Sings for his supper.
What shall we give him?
White bread and butter.
How shall he cut it
Without e'er a knife?
How shall he marry
Without e'er a wife?

HOT CROSS BUNS

Hot cross buns! Hot cross buns!
One a penny, two a penny,
Hot cross buns!
If you have no daughters,
Give them to your sons.
One a penny, two a penny,
Hot cross buns!

GOOSEY, GOOSEY GANDER

Goosey, goosey gander,
Whither shall I wander?
Upstairs and downstairs
And in my lady's chamber.
There I met an old man
Who wouldn't say his prayers.
I took him by the left leg
And threw him down the stairs.

Hickory, dickory, dock,
The mouse ran up the clock.
The clock struck one,
The mouse ran down,
Hickory, dickory, dock.

The Queen of Hearts
She made some tarts,
All on a summer's day.
The Knave of Hearts
He stole those tarts,
And took them clean away.

The King of Hearts
Called for the tarts,
And beat the knave full sore.
The Knave of Hearts
Brought back the tarts,
And vowed he'd steal no more.

Old King Cole
Was a merry old soul,
And a merry old soul was he.
He called for his pipe,
He called for his bowl,
And he called for his fiddlers three.

Now every fiddler, he had a fiddle,
And a very fine fiddle had he.
Oh, there's none so rare,
As can compare
With King Cole and his fiddlers three.

What are little boys made of, made of?
What are little boys made of?
Frogs and snails and puppy-dogs' tails,
That's what little boys are made of.

What are little girls made of, made of?
What are little girls made of?
Sugar and spice and all things nice,
That's what little girls are made of.

Little Miss Muffet
Sat on a tuffet,
Eating her curds and whey.
There came a big spider,
Who sat down beside her
And frightened Miss Muffet away.

HODDLEY, PODDLEY

Hoddley, poddley,
Puddle and fogs,
Cats are to marry
The poodle dogs.
Cats in blue jackets
And dogs in red hats,
What will become
Of the mice and the rats?

Six little mice sat down to spin.
Pussy passed by and she peeped in.
What are you doing, my little men?
Weaving coats for gentlemen.
Shall I come in and cut off your threads?
No, no, Mistress Pussy, you'd bite off our heads.
Oh, no, I'll not; I'll help you spin.
That may be so, but don't you come in.

Monday's child
is fair of face,

Tuesday's child
is full of grace,

Wednesday's child
is full of woe,

Thursday's child
has far to go,

Friday's child
is loving and giving,

Saturday's child
works hard for a living,

But the child that's born on the Sabbath day
Is bonny and blithe, and good and gay.

See-saw, Margery Daw,
Johnny shall have a new master;
He shall have but a penny a day,
Because he can't work any faster.

JACK BE NIMBLE

Jack be nimble,
Jack be quick,
Jack jump over
The candlestick.

PINS

See a pin and pick it up,
All the day you'll have good luck.
See a pin and let it lay,
Bad luck you'll have all the day.

GOING TO ST. IVES

As I was going to St. Ives,
I met a man with seven wives.
Each wife had seven sacks,
Each sack had seven cats,
Each cat had seven kits:
Kits, cats, sacks, and wives,
How many were there going to St. Ives?

One misty, moisty morning,
When cloudy was the weather,
I met a little old man
Clothed all in leather.

He began to compliment,
And I began to grin,
How do you do, and how do you do,
And how do you do again?

Three blind mice! Three blind mice!
See how they run! See how they run!
They all ran after the farmer's wife,
Who cut off their tails with a carving knife,
Did you ever see such a thing in your life,
As three blind mice?

HARK, HARK, THE DOGS DO BARK

Hark, hark, the dogs do bark,
The beggars are coming to town.
Some in rags, and some in tags,
And one in a velvet gown.

Humpty Dumpty sat on a wall,
Humpty Dumpty had a great fall.
All the King's horses and all the King's men
Couldn't put Humpty together again.

Two little dicky birds
Sitting on a wall;
One named Peter,
The other named Paul.
Fly away, Peter!
Fly away, Paul!
Come back, Peter!
Come back, Paul!

One, Two, Three, Four, Five

One, two, three, four, five,
Once I caught a fish alive.
Six, seven, eight, nine, ten,
Then I let it go again.
Why did you let it go?
Because it bit my finger so.
Which finger did it bite?
This little finger on the right.

Dance to your daddy,
My little babby,
Dance to your daddy,
My little lamb.
You shall have a fishy
In a little dishy,
You shall have a fishy
When the boat comes in.

LITTLE BO-PEEP

Little Bo-Peep has lost her sheep,
And doesn't know where to find them.
Leave them alone, and they'll come home,
Bringing their tails behind them.

POLLY PUT THE KETTLE ON

Polly put the kettle on,
Polly put the kettle on,
Polly put the kettle on,
We'll all have tea.

Sukey take it off again,
Sukey take it off again,
Sukey take it off again,
They've all gone away.

Ding, dong, bell,
Pussy's in the well.
Who put her in?
Little Johnny Green.
Who pulled her out?
Little Tommy Stout.
What a naughty boy was that
To try to drown poor pussy cat,
Who never did him any harm,
And killed the mice in his father's barn.

Hickety, Pickety, my black hen,
She lays eggs for gentlemen.
Sometimes nine and sometimes ten,
Hickety, Pickety, my black hen.

Oranges and lemons,
Say the bells of St Clement's.

You owe me five farthings,
Say the bells of St Martin's.

When will you pay me?
Say the bells of Old Bailey.

When I grow rich,
Say the bells of Shoreditch.

When will that be?
Say the bells of Stepney.

I'm sure I don't know,
Says the great bell of Bow.

Here comes a candle to light you to bed,
Here comes a chopper to chop off your head.

It's raining, it's pouring,
The old man's snoring.
He went to bed
And bumped his head
And couldn't get up in the morning.

RAIN, RAIN, GO AWAY

Rain, rain, go away,
Come again another day.
Rain, rain, go to Spain,
Never show your face again.

Rain on the green grass,
And rain on the tree,
Rain on the house-top,
But not on me.

Star Light

Star light, star bright,
First star I see tonight,
I wish I may, I wish I might,
Have the wish I wish tonight.

Yankee Doodle came to town,
Riding on a pony.
He stuck a feather in his cap
And called it macaroni.

THE MOCKING BIRD

Hush, little baby, don't say a word,
Papa's going to buy you a mocking bird.

If the mocking bird won't sing,
Papa's going to buy you a diamond ring.

If the diamond ring turns to brass,
Papa's going to buy you a looking-glass.

If the looking glass gets broke,
Papa's going to buy you a billy-goat.

If that billy-goat runs away,
Papa's going to buy you another today.

Ladybird, Ladybird, Fly Away Home

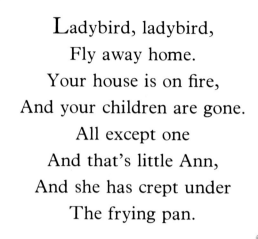

Ladybird, ladybird,
Fly away home.
Your house is on fire,
And your children are gone.
All except one
And that's little Ann,
And she has crept under
The frying pan.

Incey Wincey Spider

Incey Wincey spider
Climbing up the spout.
Down came the rain
And washed poor Incey out.

Out came the sunshine
And dried up all the rain,
So Incey Wincey spider
Climbed the spout again.

LUCY LOCKET

Lucy Locket lost her pocket,
Kitty Fisher found it.
There was not a penny in it,
Only ribbon round it.

THERE WAS A LITTLE GIRL

There was a little girl, and she had a little curl
Right in the middle of her forehead.
When she was good, she was very, very good,
But when she was bad, she was horrid.

FOR WANT OF A NAIL

For want of a nail, the shoe was lost,
For want of a shoe, the horse was lost,
For want of a horse, the rider was lost,
For want of a rider, the battle was lost,
For want of a battle, the kingdom was lost,
And all for the want of a horseshoe nail.

The Lion and the Unicorn
Were fighting for the crown.
The Lion beat the Unicorn
All around the town.

Some gave them white bread,
And some gave them brown;
Some gave them plum cake
And drummed them out of town.

HEY DIDDLE, DIDDLE

Hey diddle, diddle,
The cat and the fiddle,
The cow jumped over the moon.
The little dog laughed
To see such fun,
And the dish ran away with the spoon.

Rub-a-dub-dub,
Three men in a tub,
And who do you think they be?
The butcher, the baker,
The candlestick maker,
Turn 'em out, knaves all three.

GREGORY GRIGGS

Gregory Griggs, Gregory Griggs,
Had twenty-seven different wigs.
He wore them up, he wore them down,
To please the people of the town.
He wore them east, he wore them west,
But he never could tell which he loved the best.

CURLY LOCKS

Curly locks, curly locks,
Wilt thou be mine?
Thou shalt not wash dishes,
Nor yet feed the swine.
But sit on a cushion
And sew a fine seam,
And feed upon strawberries,
Sugar and cream.

COCK-A-DOODLE-DOO

Cock-a-doodle-doo!
My dame has lost her shoe,
My master's lost his fiddling stick
And doesn't know what to do.

Cock-a-doodle-doo!
What is my dame to do?
Till master finds his fiddling stick,
She'll dance without her shoe.

Cock-a-doodle-doo!
My dame has found her shoe,
And master's found his fiddling stick,
Sing doodle-doodle-doo!

Cock-a-doodle-doo!
My dame will dance with you,
While master fiddles his fiddling stick,
For dame and doodle-doo.

Little Boy Blue,
Come blow your horn,
The sheep's in the meadow,
The cow's in the corn.

Where is the boy
Who looks after the sheep?
He's under a haystack
Fast asleep.

Will you wake him?
No, not I!
For if I do,
He's sure to cry.

Higglety, pigglety, pop.
The dog has eaten the mop.
The pig's in a hurry,
The cat's in a flurry,
Higglety, pigglety, pop.

To market, to market,
To buy a fat pig,
Home again, home again,
Jiggety-jig.
To market, to market,
To buy a fat hog,
Home again, home again,
Jiggety-jog.

THERE WAS AN OLD WOMAN
TOSSED UP IN A BASKET

There was an old woman
Tossed up in a basket,
Seventeen times as high as the moon.
Where she was going
I couldn't but ask it,
For under her arm she carried a broom.

Old woman, old woman, old woman, said I,
Where are you going to up so high?
To brush the cobwebs off the sky!
Shall I go with you? Aye, by and by.

TWINKLE, TWINKLE, LITTLE STAR

Twinkle, twinkle, little star,
How I wonder what you are!
Up above the world so high,
Like a diamond in the sky.

PETER, PETER, PUMPKIN EATER

Peter, Peter, pumpkin eater,
Had a wife and couldn't keep her.
He put her in a pumpkin shell
And there he kept her very well.

SIMPLE SIMON

Simple Simon met a pieman,
Going to the fair.
Says Simple Simon to the pieman,
Let me taste your ware.

Says the pieman to Simple Simon,
Show me first your penny.
Says Simple Simon to the pieman,
Sir, I have not any.

Up and down the City Road,
In and out the Eagle,
That's the way the money goes,
Pop goes the weasel.

Half a pound of tuppenny rice,
Half a pound of treacle,
Mix it up and make it nice,
Pop goes the weasel.

Every night when I go out
The monkey's on the table;
Take a stick and knock it off,
Pop goes the weasel.

Bow-wow, says the dog,

Mew, mew, says the cat,

Grunt, grunt, goes the hog,

And squeak, goes the rat.

Tu-whu, says the owl,

Caw, caw, says the crow,

Quack, quack, says the duck,

And what cuckoo says you know.

IF ALL THE WORLD

If all the world were paper,
And all the sea were ink,
If all the trees were bread and cheese,
What should we have to drink?

It's enough to make a man like me
Scratch his head and think.

My father died a month ago
And left me all his riches;
A feather bed, a wooden leg,
And a pair of leather breeches.
A coffee pot without a spout,
A cup without a handle,
A tobacco pipe without a lid,
And half a farthing candle.

Georgie Porgie, pudding and pie,
Kissed the girls and made them cry.
When the boys came out to play,
Georgie Porgie ran away.

Wee Willie Winkie runs through the town,
Upstairs and downstairs in his night-gown,
Rapping at the windows, crying through the lock,
Are all the children in their beds?
For now it's eight o'clock.

Three young rats with black felt hats,

Three young ducks with white straw flats,

Three young dogs with curling tails,

Three young cats with demi-veils,

THREE YOUNG RATS

Went out to walk with three young pigs
In satin vests and sorrel wigs.
But suddenly it chanced to rain
And so they all went home again.

There was an old woman who lived in a shoe,
She had so many children she didn't know what to do.
She gave them some broth without any bread.
She whipped them all soundly and put them to bed.

CROSS PATCH

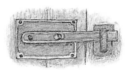

Cross patch,
Draw the latch,
Sit by the fire and spin.
Take a cup
And drink it up,
Then call your neighbours in.

ONE, TWO, BUCKLE MY SHOE

One, two,
Buckle my shoe,

Three, four,
Knock at the door,

Five, six,
Pick up sticks,

Seven, eight,
Lay them straight,

Nine, ten,
A big fat hen,

Eleven, twelve,
Dig and delve,

Thirteen, fourteen,
Maids a-courting,

Fifteen, sixteen,
Maids in the kitchen,

Seventeen, eighteen,
Maids in-waiting,

Nineteen, twenty,
My plate's empty.

BYE, BABY BUNTING

Bye, baby bunting,
Daddy's gone a-hunting,
Gone to get a rabbit skin
To wrap the baby bunting in.

THE MOON

I see the moon,
And the moon sees me.
God bless the moon,
And God bless me.

INDEX OF FIRST LINES